Mighty Mighty MONSTERS
My
MISSING
MONSTER

created by Sean O'Reilly
illustrated by Arcana Studio

Raintree

www.raintreepublishers.co.uk
Visit our website to find out
more information about
Raintree books.

To order:
☎ Phone 0845 6044371
📠 Fax +44 (0) 1865 312263
📧 Email myorders@raintreepublishers.co.uk

Customers from outside the UK please telephone +44 1865 312262

Raintree is an imprint of Capstone Global Library Limited,
a company incorporated in England and Wales having its registered
office at 7 Pilgrim Street, London, EC4V 6LB
– Registered company number: 6695582

First published by Stone Arch Books in 2010
First published in the United Kingdom in paperback in 2012
The moral rights of the proprietor have been asserted.

Edited by Laura Knowles
Originated by Capstone Global Library Ltd
Printed and bound in China by South China Printing Company

ISBN 978 1 406 23722 1 (paperback)
16 15 14 13 12
10 9 8 7 6 5 4 3 2 1

British Library Cataloguing in Publication Data
A full catalogue record for this book is available
from the British Library.

In a strange corner of the world known as Transylmania . . .

Legendary monsters were born.

WELCOME TO TRANSYLMANIA

But long before their frightful fame, these classic creatures faced fears of their own.

To take on terrifying teachers and homework horrors,
they formed the most fearsome friendship on Earth . . .

Vlad

Talbot

Witchita

Milton

Poto

Frankie

Igor

Mary

9

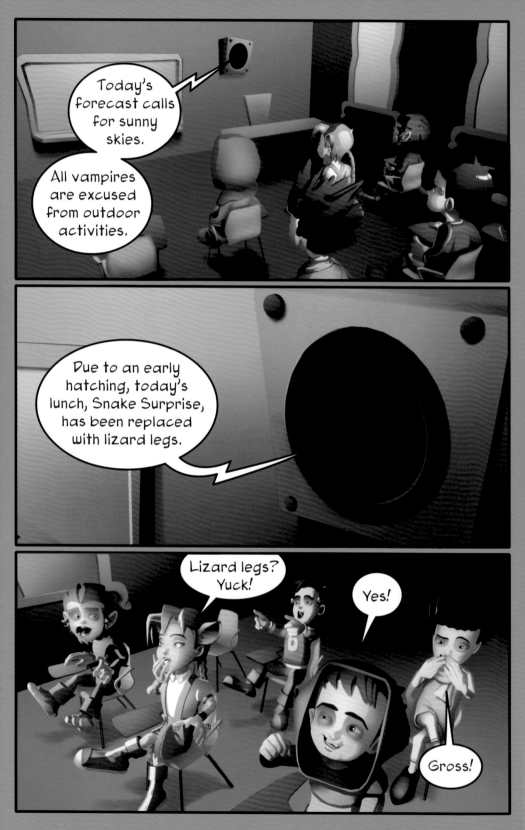

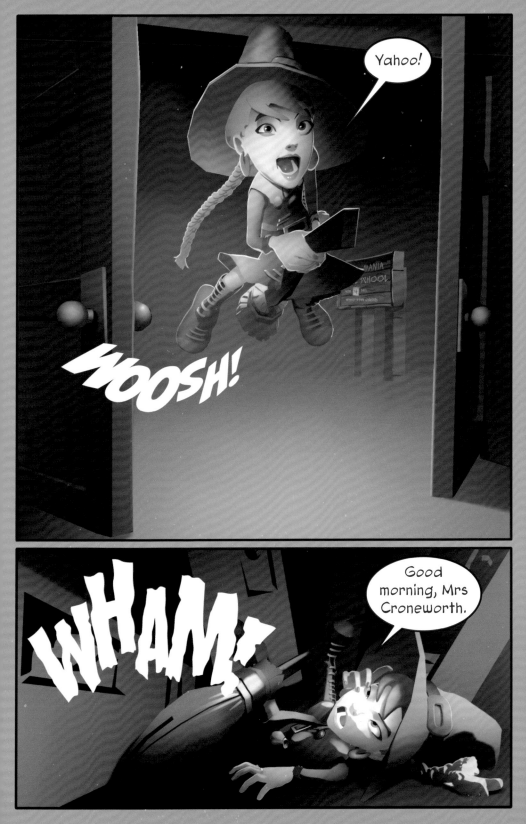

21

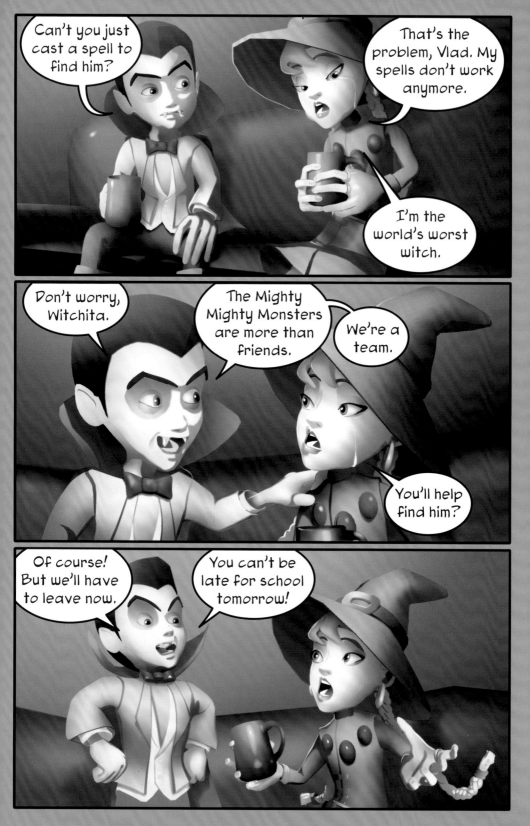

32

35

That morning in class . . .
Bring your pet to school day!!
Excellent work, Witchita!
A+
I couldn't have done it without my friends . . .
And that includes you, Creech!

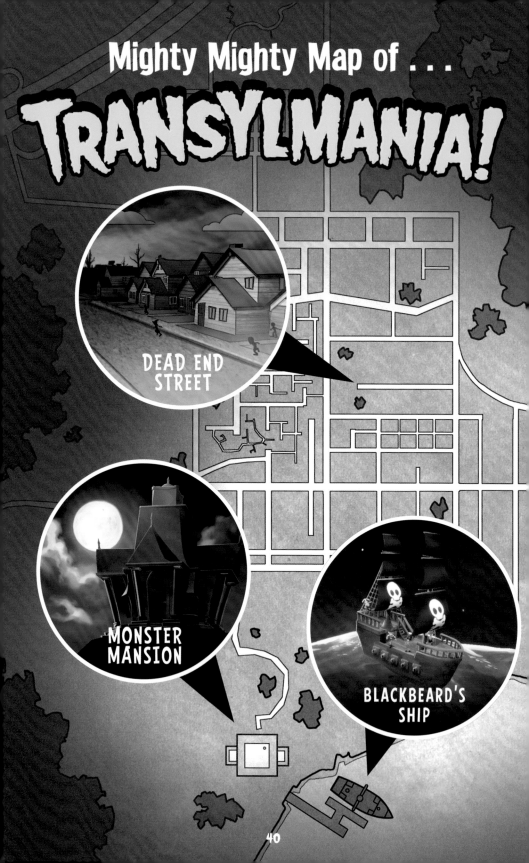

SPOOKY FOREST

MONSTER SCHOOL

FLAME OF HALLOWEEN

CASTLE OF DOOM

41

Mighty Mighty
MONSTERS

...BEFORE THEY WERE STARS!

WITCHITA AND CREECH

Nicknames: Witchy and Fire Breath

Hometown: Transylmania

Favourite colour: black

Favourite animal: black Cats

Mighty mighty powers: Witchita has magical superpowers; Creech has the ability to breathe fire; together, they are unstoppable.

BIOGRAPHY

As a young magic maker, Witchita struggled to control her powers. At age two, she turned her babysitter into a cockroach. Unfortunately, these early failures left Witchita with little confidence. But, as a member of the Mighty Mighty Monsters, she quickly got it back. Along with her super pet Creech, Witchita is one of the most powerful members of the ghoulish gang. As an adult, Witchita headed to Hollywood, where she instructed some of the greatest witches of all time.

WHERE ARE THEY NOW?

Author L. Frank Baum created the Wicked Witch of the West for his children's book *The Wonderful Wizard of Oz*. In 1931, the book was adapted into a film, making the character one of the scariest witches of all time.

Of course, not all witches are evil. In his children's book, Baum also created two good witches: The Good Witch of the South and the Good Witch of the North. However, only the latter appears in the film adaptation.

Today, witches are still popular in books and films. In J. K. Rowling's bestselling *Harry Potter* series, students study to become wizards and witches.

ABOUT SEAN O'REILLY
AND ARCANA STUDIO

As a lifelong comics fan, Sean O'Reilly dreamed of becoming a comic book creator. In 2004, he realized that dream by creating Arcana Studio. In one short year, O'Reilly took his studio from a one-person operation in his house to an award-winning comic book publisher with more than 150 graphic novels produced for Harper Collins, Simon & Schuster, Random House, Scholastic, and others.

Within a year, the company won many awards including the Shuster Award for Outstanding Publisher and the Moonbeam Award for top children's graphic novel. O'Reilly also won the Top 40 Under 40 award from the city of Vancouver and authored *The Clockwork Girl* for Top Graphic Novel at Book Expo America in 2009.

Currently, O'Reilly is one of the most prolific independent comic book writers in Canada. While showing no signs of slowing down in comics, he now also writes screenplays and adapts his creations for the big screen.

GLOSSARY

accomplish do something successfully

announcement thing said officially or publicly, as over a radio or loudspeaker

confidence strong belief in your own abilities

DJ short for "disc jockey", or an announcer on a radio show

excuse reason given to explain why you have done something wrong

forecast prediction of what will happen in the future

scent odour trail left by an animal

talent natural ability or skill

tone deaf unable to hear the difference in musical pitch

DISCUSSION QUESTIONS

1. All of the Mighty Mighty Monsters helped Witchita find her pet. Which team member helped the most? Explain your answer.

2. Each page of this graphic novel has several illustrations. These illustrations are called panels. Which panel in this book is your favourite? Why?

3. All of the Mighty Mighty Monsters are different. Which character do you like the best? Why?

WRITING PROMPTS

1. Have you ever had a pet? If so, write a story about your pet. If not, write about a pet that you would like to have.

2. In this story, the Mighty Mighty Monsters helped out a friend. Describe a time that you helped a friend or family member.

3. Write your own Mighty Mighty Monsters adventure. What will the ghoulish gang do next? What villains will they face? You decide.

FIND OUT MORE

INFORMATION BOOKS

The Mystery of Vampires and Werewolves
(Can Science Solve?), Chris Oxlade (Heinemann
Library, 2008)

Vampires and the Undead (Dark Side), Anita Ganeri
(Wayland, 2010)

GRAPHIC NOVELS

Dracula (Graphic Revolve), Bram Stoker, retold by
Michael Burgan (Raintree, 2009)

Frankenstein (Graphic Revolve), Mary Shelley, retold
by Michael Burgan (Raintree, 2009)

Werewolf (Graphic Chillers), Jeff Zornow (Franklin
Watts, 2010)

WEBSITE

learnenglishkids.britishcouncil.org/en/make-
your-own/make-your-monster
Visit this website to create your own monster. You
can also invent your own scary story, dangerous
animal, or superhero.

Mighty Mighty MONSTERS
ADVENTURES

Monster Mansion
ISBN: 978 1 406 23721 4

New Monster in School
ISBN: 978 1 406 23723 8

Hide and Shriek
ISBN: 978 1 406 23718 4

The King of Halloween Castle
ISBN: 978 1 406 23719 1

Lost in Spooky Forest
ISBN: 978 1 406 23720 7